5/10/84

To
Melanie
from
G. Ma Lewis

SLEEKY

Illustrations by JOSEPH CAPOZIO

the otter

RHODA LEONARD
WILLIAM S. BRISCOE

CALIFORNIA STATE SERIES
Published by
CALIFORNIA STATE DEPARTMENT OF EDUCATION
Sacramento, 1969

TABLE OF CONTENTS

ALTHOUGH he does not know it, Sleeky the otter became a friend of mine one summer when my family and I were staying at a cabin deep in the north country woods. We were guests of John Miller, a friend of ours who was game warden for the area.

At first the woods around John's cabin seemed empty and lonely. But soon I found that one had only to move softly and keep his eyes open to get to know the animals that lived there. This was how I met Sleeky the otter. I called him Sleeky because of his coat of fur. His fur was always sleek, shiny and smooth when he came out of the water. Sleeky was often in the water. It was his playground and his hunting ground.

It took a long time to learn about Sleeky and his family. But the time was well spent. Part of the story of Sleeky I learned on my own. Part I learned later from John.

this is the story of that otter

SLEEKY the otter

1

THE CUBS

SLEEKY AND HIS MATE found their way to Miller's Pond one fall day. It was a cold day and very, very clear. The sun shone on the bright fall leaves. It made the water look silver. The two otters were swimming down the stream that ran into Miller's Pond. As they swam, their dark brown heads broke through the bright water. They were swimming slowly. Often they played and splashed in the water. But all at once they saw the pond. Then they started to swim as fast as they could. When they saw it had a mud bank, they began to chatter. They sounded very happy. They climbed out of the water and bounded to the highest place on the bank. Sleeky got there first.

Right away Sleeky started to clear a kind of trail. It went from the top of the bank straight down to the water. His mate helped him. When they were through, Sleeky climbed to the top of the bank. He turned and faced the water. Then he turned his feet back and pushed. Whizz! Down he slid into the water. Almost before he could climb out again, his mate did the very same thing! Nose first she, too, splashed into the water.

The otters' wet, brown fur looked smooth and bright as they came out of the water. They climbed to the top of the slide and faced the water again. Again and again they slid into the water. Their wet bodies smoothed the mud slide. Each time they slid into the water, they went faster than before. Sometimes they chased after each other under the water. A trail of bubbles on top of the water showed where they swam.

Once while they were swimming, some bright fall leaves landed on the water. Sleeky caught the biggest one as soon as it landed. He rolled over on his back. Then he began to pass it from paw to paw. His mate tried to get it away from him. She chased him around the pond. Sometimes Sleeky almost let her catch him. But just as she swam near, he would swim away as fast as he could. When they were tired of this game, they went back to their slide. But they never seemed to get tired of playing.

The otters were the only animals in these woods that were not busy getting ready for winter. Many squirrels ran about chattering. The squirrels were busy hunting for food to put away for the winter months. The birds that had not left the woods for the winter were busy, too. The birds hunted through piles of leaves looking for insects. Beavers were in their ponds making their huts ready for winter.

Not far away, some bears, already fat, were looking for still more food. The bears were eating all they could. This was to last them through their long winter sleep. For months, the bears would not eat anything at all.

But Sleeky and his mate did not care about getting ready for winter. They always seemed to be at play. They stopped their games only long enough to eat and sleep.

It was not long after the two otters found Miller's Pond that the first snow fell. It covered the ground with a soft white. It piled high on the trees. The snow and cold turned the woods into a quiet place. The pond was almost all covered with ice. Even the streams that had bubbled all summer long were quiet under the silver ice.

Many insects and animals were sleeping safe from the snow and cold. But the otters were still as busy as ever. They had made a new slide in the same place as the old one. It was a snow slide. The snow made a very fast slide. It was smooth as glass. Down the otters slid into piles of soft, white snow. In the middle of the pond, where there was no ice, they swam. They climbed out of the water and ran to the top of the slide for another turn.

Sometimes the otters ran after each other through the snow. They rolled in the snow. They jumped into snow banks. Then out they climbed. Then they rolled in the snow some more.

The two otters never even felt the cold. Their bodies were covered by warm coats of fur. And they had another coat under their fur. This was a coat of fat. This coat of fat kept them warm on the coldest days and in the coldest water. They liked cold winters, for the snow and ice made new places to play.

Sleeky and his mate played in the snow all winter. They swam in the pond to catch fish. Sometimes they stayed under the ice for a very long time. It seemed they would never come up. They knew where they could find open places in the ice. And they could find air bubbles under the ice when they needed them. They put their noses into the bubbles and breathed the air trapped there.

Near the end of winter, Sleeky and his mate moved to a larger pond. It was up the stream from Miller's Pond. There the female otter found an empty muskrat nest. The nest was under a bank at the side of the pond. The muskrat had left it long before. The female otter looked the nest over with more care than any place she had seen before. This empty nest seemed to be more than just a good sleeping place to her. She went into it and came out again many times.

Sleeky swam over to the nest. He wanted to look in, too. But his mate pushed him away. He looked surprised. He tried again to go in. This time the female chased him back into the pond!

Sleeky could not understand why his mate seemed to be so angry with him. What had happened to her? She had never been like this before. He did not want her to be angry with him. So he swam around in the middle of the pond where there was open water. There he put on a show. He splashed and rolled in the water. He swam in circles. He chattered and whistled to his mate, but she went on with her work.

She worked long and hard getting the nest ready. First she went to work on the tunnel. It went a long way back into the bank. She did not want the tunnel to be so long. So she made a small room nearer to the water. From this room she began to dig another tunnel that opened up on land. The ground was still cold and very hard. It took a long time to dig it away. Still she worked at it. At last her tunnel opened into the one that the muskrat had made.

Next she pulled sticks and leaves and grasses from the pond into the nest. She placed them carefully in the small room she had made. The leaves and grasses made a soft cover on top of the sticks. At last she smoothed the snow in front of the nest. She was afraid signs of her work might show enemy animals where the nest was. Now she was happy with her work. She lay down in the little room and closed her eyes. Soon she was sleeping.

All this time Sleeky was swimming around the pond. He was still waiting for his mate to come out and play with him. He could not understand what she liked so much about an empty nest. He was not able to see anything so good about it. There were so many more things to do outside. There was still snow to play in and ice to swim under or slide on.

At last his mate woke up and came out of the nest. But she came out only to find food. She walked out on the ice as far as she could go. Something silver swam by under the ice. The female swam after it. After a moment she came to the top of the water with a fish in her mouth. She climbed back up on the ice and ate it quickly.

Sleeky was so happy to see her that he rolled over and over in the water. He climbed up on the ice to rub noses with her. He wanted her to know how happy he was to see her. Then he went back into the water. He caught a big, fat fish and put it at her feet. He watched while she took it to the bank and ate it. As soon as he saw she was through, Sleeky bounded off over the snow. How could she help but play with him now? But when he looked around, he saw her swimming in the pond again.

He headed back and found her looking for more food. She did not seem to see or hear him. She just went on eating. When she was through, she turned and went back into the nest.

Now Sleeky was very angry. He left the pond as fast as he could.

That night he went to sleep in a hollow log near the pond. When he woke up the next morning, he was no longer angry. He whistled to his mate. Then he went back to the bank to wait for her. He saw her many times that day. But she would not play.

Sleeky still stayed near the pond. He made the hollow log his sleeping place. He saw his mate only now and then.

One morning she came out to feed before the sun was up. Sleeky called to her. Just then squeaking sounds came from the nest. The female ran back into the tunnel. The squeaking sounds stopped.

Now, at last, Sleeky could understand. He knew why his mate seemed to like the nest so much. She was now a mother. Her cubs were there under the bank, in that nest!

Sleeky still felt very much alone. But he was not angry any more. Left to himself, he traveled up and down the stream. He always came back to the pond where the nest was. When he was near the pond, the hollow log was his sleeping place. Sometimes he would be away for a day or two. Then he would show up again at the pond and sleep in his hollow log.

One day he was swimming in the open water in the middle of the pond. Only his head showed out of the water. He was watching the bank straight in front of him. He could not see as far or as well as many other animals. Still he liked to watch dark shadows of trees play over the white snow. It was a bright, clear day and the shadows were very dark and sharp.

One shadow moved strangely. This shadow moved away from the trees. It moved over the white snow very slowly. The otter watched it carefully. He saw that it was a large bobcat. The bobcat's ears stood straight up. He held his head high. All at once he nosed the snow. He seemed to be hunting for something. Again he lifted his head and stood very still. He was very near the nest.

Sleeky was not afraid. The bobcat was no danger to him as long as he stayed in the water. The otter was not even afraid for his mate and cubs. They were safe under the ground in their nest. Sleeky watched quietly to see what the bobcat would do next.

The bobcat began to dig at the ground. He was digging near the land tunnel to the nest! Now Sleeky began to be afraid. This big animal was much too near Sleeky's family for the otter's liking. The otter swam to the ice as quickly as he could. He was angry. He called to the bobcat. The bobcat stopped digging and turned with a start. The next moment, Sleeky climbed up on the ice and ran straight toward the bobcat!

2
MANY
CLOSE CALLS

FOR A MOMENT the bobcat stood still, not knowing what was happening. His sharp ears had heard some squeaks under the snow. He thought there might be small animals there. He had been trying to find where the squeaks came from. Then there had been a loud cry from the pond. Now this little brown animal was heading straight for him!

It looked like an otter. The bobcat was more surprised than ever. He had seen otters before. Otters were animals that stayed out of his way. But this one was heading for him. And he was running fast! The bobcat was far too hungry to stay still for more than a moment. He bounded to the pond to catch the otter.

This was just what Sleeky wanted him to do. Now the otter turned quickly and ran on the ice near the bank. The bobcat followed on the bank. The bobcat could run faster than the otter. He came closer and closer to Sleeky. At last the bobcat was very close. All he needed to do was spring from the bank to the ice. Then he could land right on top of the otter.

But Sleeky knew what he was doing. Before he could be caught, he turned. He went as far as he could on the ice. He stood on the ice and faced the angry bobcat. Then he began to call and whistle to him.

The bobcat watched the otter from the bank. He could see that Sleeky was only about two big jumps away. There was no open water close for the otter to jump into. They had come to the other end of the pond, and the open water was quite far away. Still the bobcat did not spring. There was no snow on the ice between him and the otter. The silver ice looked as smooth as glass.

As Sleeky called, the bobcat grew more and more angry. At last he was so angry and so hungry that he did not think about the ice. He jumped from the bank.

When he landed, his feet slipped out from under him. Down he went! He lay hissing on the cold, cold ice! He slipped and slid as he tried to get up. He was very angry. When he hissed, his sharp teeth shone.

Sleeky did not stay to watch. This was what he had been waiting for. Now he ran over the ice. He headed for the bank again. He did not slip because his feet were made for climbing on wet rocks or walking on ice.

He did not stop at the bank but bounded away from the pond. Then he followed a stream that ran out of it. Not all of the stream was covered with ice. He could see open water before him. He was making the bobcat follow him far, far away from his mate.

Soon he was far enough away to be safe. By now the bobcat had stopped thinking about the squeaks under the snow. Now all he could think about was catching Sleeky. But by this time Sleeky was finding the chase fun. It was a kind of game to him. As long as he could stay in the stream, he felt safe. He did not want to get away from the bobcat just yet. He was having fun now, and he wanted the game to go on longer. He called to the bobcat to follow him. The sounds he made now were bright chattering sounds. He sounded very much as though he were calling his mate to come and play.

But the bobcat was not playing! This was no game to him. He was hungry and that made him go on. He had not found much to eat this winter. His need for food was great. The otter was food. So after the bobcat climbed back on the bank, he chased after the otter again.

Once Sleeky did a very strange thing. He caught a fish. But he did not eat it. He kept it in his mouth. When he saw the bobcat start to move away from the bank, Sleeky came out of the water. He placed the fish on the bank. Then he jumped back into the water.

The bobcat smelled the fish. He turned around and ran to the fish. Then he ate it. All the while, Sleeky stayed in the water. He chattered to himself. This was fun. It was all a great big game to him. And it made the bobcat want to keep on following him.

The stream was now growing wider. Here there was not as much ice. Sleeky started to swim under the water more often. Sometimes he stayed under for a long time. He found many fish in the stream. He was tired of the chase. Soon he no longer looked for the bobcat. He did not even know when the bobcat stopped trying to catch him and went away into the woods.

Sleeky swam on down the stream. He was now far away from his mate and her nest. Soon he came to a large pond. Here there were still piles of snow on the ground. But there was no ice on the water.

Sleeky knew at once what kind of pond this was. Small huts of sticks and mud were sticking out of the water. At one end was a dam of logs and sticks. The dam and the smell about the place made it clear that this was a beaver pond. It had been made when the beavers put the dam together. But now there were no beavers around. Sleeky could see that the dam was broken at one end. And one of the huts looked as though it were falling over. Sleeky was very happy with this pond. An empty beaver pond was just the kind of place he liked. The huts made good sleeping places. Around the logs in the dam and near the mud banks of the pond he would find food. He would find snakes and insects and all kinds of small water animals.

Sleeky rolled and turned in the water just because he was so happy. Near the dam, he caught a snake. Then he made his way under water to one of the beaver huts. He was tired after his chase. A good sleep was just what he wanted. He swam near the hut. He was looking for a way to swim into it.

All at once he stopped! There was a dark shadow between him and the hut! He swam closer. He saw that it was a muskrat. At first he was ready to chase the muskrat away. He wanted this pond for himself.

Sleeky swam closer still. He could not understand why the muskrat did not move. He nosed it. Still it did not move. Then all at once the fur on Sleeky's back stood up. One leg of the muskrat was caught in a trap. The muskrat was held under water by the trap.

Sleeky knew about traps. His mother had been caught in one. His father had been caught in another one when he went to try and save the mother. The day that his mother and father were caught, Sleeky had learned a hard lesson. Where there was one trap, there could be more. And traps are an otter's enemy.

Where were the other traps? Sleeky could not see any signs of them. He wanted more than anything to get out of that pond. But how could he know where to turn? A trap might be waiting for him any place!

He was afraid. He wanted to swim deep to get away from danger. But the deep water of this pond held a muskrat caught in a trap. What could he do? There was only one thing left. He would swim near the top of the water and go out of the pond the way he had come into it. Then he might be safe. He had seen no signs of traps there. He began to swim back.

Just then he heard the loud cry of a bird. He stopped swimming in time to see a man coming out of the woods. The man carried a gun. A brown dog followed him.

Here was new danger! Sleeky slipped his head under the water. He was afraid to swim deep because of the traps. He was afraid to show himself on top of the water. Then the man might see him. Again he did the only thing he could do. He stayed as still as he could with only his nose out of the water. He was so still that not even a bubble showed on the water.

Sleeky stayed where he was for a long time. He was so still that the man did not see him. Even the dog had not seen him yet.

The man put his gun down next to a log. "Stay, boy," he said to the dog.

The dog lay down by the gun. "You stay away from the traps, boy!" the man said. He rubbed the dog's ears. "*You* would not make a very good catch!"

The man walked to the pond. He looked carefully at the ground and the water near it. At one place, he started to dig into a pile of snow. He pulled up a trap. He put the trap back and covered it again with snow. He smoothed the snow over it. Then he looked at the far side of the pond.

"Could be that some traps on the other side would have caught something," he said out loud.

All this time, Sleeky had hardly moved. The otter did not see the traps. He did not know what the man was doing.

Sleeky could not know that he would have been safe in deep water after all. All the traps were at the bank.

Each one was held to the ground by a chain and a large spike. When an animal was caught, it tried to pull away from the trap. Often an animal pulled the trap into the water. Then it tried to get away by swimming. It would pull the chain as far as it would go. Then the spike held it fast. The trap held the animal under the water so it could not breathe.

But Sleeky did not know a thing about all this. He knew only what he saw. He saw a muskrat in a trap in deep water. This made it quite clear to him that there was danger right there.

At last Sleeky looked out of the water again. He saw the dog come over to the man. The man was pulling a chain and trap out of the water. In the trap was a muskrat. Now Sleeky was more afraid than ever! Traps seemed to be every place. He was so afraid that he was no longer careful. He just wanted to get away! He turned and swam to the other side of the pond.

As soon as Sleeky started to move, the dog saw him. He began to bark. The loud barking made Sleeky even more afraid.

Now the man saw Sleeky, too. He ran to the log and picked up his gun. He lifted the gun and fired it at the dark head in the water.

The otter was very near the far bank. He heard the gun go off. Then something splashed in the water near him. Sleeky climbed up the bank. The gun sounded again. This time, something whizzed very close over his back.

Sleeky did not hear the gun go off again. But he heard the man's voice. The man was calling loudly. "Back, boy!" he called. "Come back! You are too near the traps!"

While the man was trying to keep the dog from the traps, Sleeky got away. He ran into the woods. The otter ran and ran until he could no longer hear the man's voice. Then he knew he was not being followed.

Now Sleeky was very far from his mate and her nest. Between him and his family were many enemies. A bobcat, traps, a man, and a dog were between them. Sleeky wanted only to get away from danger. And danger lay behind him. The otter could not turn back.

3
SLEEKY
COMES BACK

FOR ABOUT A MONTH, Sleeky wandered from stream to stream. He did not even seem to think about his mate and the nest. He was happy to be wandering. And his mate was so busy with her cubs that she did not have time to think about Sleeky.

Sleeky's mate had two cubs — a male and a female. It took all her time just to feed and care for them. Otter cubs do not open their eyes until they are almost a month old. They need their mother's milk. Even though their little bodies are covered by coats of soft brown fur, they need to be near her warm body. The mother otter would leave her nest only long enough to find food.

Before the little otters were one month old, their eyes opened. As the days went by, their eyes and bodies grew stronger. Often they rolled and played together in the little room. By the time spring came, their mother saw that they were too big to stay in the nest all day. It was time to take them out into the world. Each day she let them play in the outside world for longer and longer times.

Now, caring for the cubs was a bigger job than ever. The outside world held so many new and strange things for them to see and do. Because they wanted to hunt out every new thing they saw, heard or smelled, their mother had to watch them carefully. They could run right into danger!

Now and then, their mother did have to go into the pond to catch fish. But she left her cubs on the bank and never swam too far from them. One warm spring day while she was swimming, the cubs were playing near some high grass by the nest. The cubs stopped playing when the grass began to move. They were not able to see what was making it move. The cubs tried to be good and stay where they were in the clearing. They had already learned how angry their mother could be when they went off too far alone. Still, they wanted to know why the grass moved.

Quietly, the little otters walked into the grass. Then they backed out of the high grass so quickly that they fell over. They squeaked and chattered. In a moment their mother was out of the pond and by their side. At once she saw why her cubs were afraid. There in the grass was a very large snake!

The mother otter knew just what to do. She coughed to warn the cubs to stay back and be quiet. Then she circled the snake slowly. The snake kept its eyes on her. It moved its head from side to side. It watched every move she made. Every time the mother otter circled near enough, the snake tried to strike her. When the snake's head came at her, the otter jumped away.

The mother otter wanted the snake to strike at her. She was watching and waiting for the right time. She would close in after one strike, before the snake had time to strike again!

She watched carefully, but the right time did not seem to come. This snake was too big and too quick for her. Still she kept circling.

Just then a dark brown animal came running down the bank. The animal was chattering loudly. The mother otter never took her eyes off the snake. Still, she knew at once that this animal was her mate. He had come back at last.

As soon as Sleeky saw what was happening, he began to help. The two otters worked together. They kept moving in a circle with the snake in the middle. Now when the snake tried to strike one of them, the other could close in from behind. The snake could not keep its eyes on both otters at once. Soon it began to tire. It was not long before Sleeky had the snake by the back of its head. He bit it hard with his sharp teeth. When the snake stopped moving, Sleeky let it fall to the ground.

The mother and father otter were very happy to be together again. They rubbed noses because they were so happy. They chattered and chattered.

At first, the little otters watched quietly. They did not make a sound. They just watched the two big otters. They did not know what to think of the strange otter. Never in their young lives had they seen any other otter but their mother.

But the cubs could not stay still for long. They nosed the snake and began to chatter. The snake did not move. So they left it alone. Then they came over to look at their father. Sleeky looked down and rubbed his nose on the little male's head. The cub backed away and hissed. The cubs looked at their mother with wide, surprised eyes.

Sleeky wanted to play. He started to chase the cubs for fun. At first the cubs were afraid. They ran from him. Then Sleeky turned. He chattered to the cubs to chase him. Soon the otters were following him. When he turned, they turned. When he rolled on the ground, they did the same. They thought this game was great fun!

Now that Sleeky was with his family again, things were not the same. He did not stay with them in the nest. Yet he was always there when his mate and cubs came outside. He helped watch the cubs. He played with them. He helped the mother to fish.

Sleeky often took his family quite far from the nest. He took them on many trips to new places on the bank around the pond. One day he took them all the way to the stream that ran out of the pond.

The mother was not very happy about this trip. While they were on the trip, she kept looking back at the nest. But the young ones bounded off to keep up with their father. The mother was afraid that a cub might wander away. They still needed her for their food. And they had not yet learned how to swim. She was not happy until they went back to the nest.

The mother otter could see that she had a new big job to do. The cubs must learn some new lessons. The next morning the lessons began. When the young ones came to her for milk, she pushed them away. She went outside without feeding them. The cubs were hungry. They followed after their mother. They could not understand why she did not feed them. They squeaked and cried. She did not seem to hear them. Without even looking around, she slipped into the water. The angry and hungry cubs lay down on the bank.

Soon the mother came to the bank with a fat, little fish in her mouth. She placed it on the ground in front of the cubs. Then, before the cubs could come to her again for milk, she went back into the water. Soon she placed another fish on the ground. Sleeky saw what his mate was trying to do, so he worked with her. He, too, caught a fish.

The little male went over to the last fish. It still moved. He pushed it with his nose. He wanted to play with it. He pushed at it with his paw. He turned it over. Then he passed it from paw to paw. He put his head to one side and looked up at his father.

Now Sleeky picked up the fish. He bit it into pieces with his sharp teeth. He swallowed one of the pieces. Then he put the other pieces in front of the cubs.

The cubs had been watching all this very carefully. Now each one swallowed a piece of fish, too. To their surprise, they liked it. Their father bit some more pieces of fish for them. Now they ate almost all the fish that had been caught.

After a while their mother did let them have some milk. But the next day she caught more fish for them. She started feeding them frogs, too. Soon they no longer needed her milk at all. They ate fish, frogs, and insects. This food would help them grow big and strong.

Now it was time for the cubs to learn another lesson. This new lesson would help them to grow up even more than the first. The young ones would have to learn to swim.

First their mother and father took them to the water. The big otters went right into the water. They called the young ones to follow. But the young ones stayed well away from the water on the bank.

The big otters swam on their backs and called the cubs to come to them. The cubs knew what their mother and father wanted. But they were afraid of the water. They just watched the big otters.

At last Sleeky rolled over quickly. He swam under the water, leaving a trail of bubbles on top. Soon he came up near the bank with a fat fish in his mouth.

The little female tried to take the fish from her father. But Sleeky backed away. Then once again he held out the fish. This time both cubs tried to take it. When Sleeky backed away, the cubs slipped. Splash! They both landed in the water!

The cubs had never been so afraid of anything. The water closed over their heads! It made a roaring sound in their ears. They could not see. When they cried for help, they swallowed some of the cold water.

In a moment, the cubs came up to the top of the water, coughing and crying. As they splashed they swallowed some more water. Still their mother and father let them splash around a little. Then the big otters let the cubs climb on their backs.

Their mother and father swam around the pond with the wet little cubs on their backs. Soon the cubs were no longer afraid. They even began to like being up on the big otters' backs. After a while their mother and father took them back to the bank.

Soon the mother and father called the young ones into the water again. At first the cubs stood on the bank. But after a moment they slipped into the pond without any help. To their surprise they found that they were swimming.

The little male was very happy with himself. He rolled over and over in the water. When he stopped rolling, he found that he was able to stay on top of the water. The little female had already climbed up on her mother's back. Now the little male climbed up on his father's back.

This time, though, when they were near the middle of the pond, they were pushed off. Then the big otters swam quickly out of the way. The young ones had to swim all the way to the bank alone. They swam well. The big otters were very happy with them.

4
INTO
A WIDER WORLD

THE NEXT MORNING when the mother otter woke the sun was not up yet. The woods were dark and still. Far off, a bird's cry broke through the quiet. Then all was still again.

The mother otter went through the tunnel to the pond. She looked around to see that all was safe outside. She lifted her head and smelled the air. Then she went back into the nest and woke the cubs.

Right away, the cubs ran to the tunnel that opened up on land. But their mother pulled them back. Then she pushed both cubs through the other tunnel—the one that opened into the pond.

The cubs stopped as soon as they came to the water. They chattered at their mother and tried to turn back. The mother pushed them into the water. Again the water closed over their heads. But this time they did not try to fight. They did not swallow any water.

In a moment they came to the top of the water. They were no longer afraid of the water. They liked it!

The cubs swam well, but they tired quite quickly. They climbed out on the bank. They rolled on the ground to dry their wet fur. Their mother rubbed her nose on their heads softly. Then she went into the water and caught some fish for them. As she put one fish on the bank, she could hear Sleeky whistle. She whistled back to him. Soon he swam up to his family. The two big otters swam and played together in the water while the cubs played on the bank.

All at once the big otters swam under the water. All the cubs could see was a trail of silver bubbles where their mother and father had been. Then they saw some bubbles in a new place, and up came the big otters again.

At last the mother and father otters called the cubs into the water. This time the cubs jumped right in. They swam and swam. But they did not try to swim under water.

Now each big otter took a young one on its back. The cubs thought this was a very good game. Then, all at once, to the cubs' surprise, the big otters swam under water!

Deeper and deeper the big otters swam. The cubs held on with all their might. They did not even try to breathe. The water roared in their ears. At last the big otters came up for air. The cubs did not let go of their fur. Again, without warning, the big otters went under. Again and again they swam under water and came up for air. Once, when they were very deep, each big otter made a quick turn. Off fell the cubs! Before they even knew what had happened, the cubs were swimming under water!

At last summer came to the woods. Sleeky and his mate felt like wandering once again. They had been in this pond long enough. Their young ones had already learned to swim. The cubs were as happy in the water as on land. They did not need their mother's milk. And they could catch fish and frogs without help. They were old enough to travel. Now the otter family could go out into a wider world.

First the little family followed the stream that ran out of the pond. They followed the stream slowly, stopping many times to eat or play. At one place, where there was a mud bank, they made a slide. One after the other, nose first, the big and little otters whizzed into the water!

After the game was over, they went on down the stream. Soon they came to a pond with beaver huts. The huts seemed to be empty. To the mother and the cubs, this looked like a very good place to stay.

But all at once the father otter began to do a strange thing. He swam around the cubs, pushing them to the bank. He chattered and called to the mother otter. He would not let his family go into the pond. He chattered his warning to them again and again. He was afraid of the traps he had seen when he was here before. He started off into the woods. The mother otter and the little female followed him.

Only the little male stayed back. He liked ponds. He did not seem to hear his father's warning. He saw a fish swim by near the bank. He started after it! Then there was a clanking sound! The cub let out a sharp cry. Something held him by the leg!

The harder he tried to pull away, the more his leg hurt. The little cub was very much afraid. Not ever had anything hurt him so much. His eyes were wide, and he squeaked and cried. Sleeky ran back to the cub. He knew at once why the little one cried out. The cub was caught in a trap.

Sleeky picked the cub up in his mouth and tried to carry him. But there was a chain on the trap. The chain was held fast to a large spike in the ground. The chain was not very long, and Sleeky could not move the cub very far.

Sleeky put the cub back down on the ground. Then he bit at the chain. But the chain was harder and stronger than Sleeky's teeth. Still he bit at it. By this time his mate had run back to him. She tried to pull at the spike. The other little cub just stood back and watched.

Sleeky grew more and more angry. At last he bit the chain so hard that he broke one of his teeth! Still he would not stop trying to save his cub. Just then the bark of a dog sounded in the woods. Both Sleeky and his mate stopped pulling at the chain.

Then the mother otter pushed the little female behind a big rock. Sleeky stayed by the trap even when the barks sounded very close. Soon a little dog came running through the woods. Sleeky thought of the dog that had barked at him last winter. He was afraid of dogs. But now he was trying to save his cub. He ran at the dog with all his might. He bit him on the leg. He was very angry and he was fighting hard.

This dog was very young. He was surprised. He had not wanted to fight. He only wanted to know what all the strange sounds were about. But he pulled himself to his feet. Now he, too, was angry. While Sleeky and the dog were fighting, the mother otter again pulled at the chain. This time the spike came out of the soft ground. Now the little male could move very slowly by pulling the trap. The mother otter called to the little female to follow her. The mother otter wanted her cubs far, far away from the pond. She ran on with the little female close behind. But the trapped cub went very slowly. The trap caught on rocks and sticks. The little cub fell to the ground. He was breathing hard. His leg did not hurt so much when he did not move. He did not want to get up again. But his mother knew he must keep moving. They must all get far away from the beaver pond!

The mother came back and tried to lift her cub. But she could not carry the trap, too. She put him down again. She stopped and lifted her head. She heard a new sound over the sounds of Sleeky and the dog. She heard a deep voice. A man had walked out of the woods! He called to his dog. When Sleeky saw the man, he backed away from the dog. He ran into the woods when the man picked the dog up. Still he did not follow his mate and cubs. He did not want the man to know where they were. Sleeky watched the man from the woods.

The man looked at the dog's leg. He saw where Sleeky had bit him. "That must hurt," he said to the dog. "But you are all right. That must have been a father otter. His family must be around here." He put the dog down and rubbed its head.

After a moment he stood up and looked around. The little male otter was trying to move again. The trap clanked on a rock. The cub cried out. The man and dog followed the sound! The man seemed to know what it was. As the man got to the trap, the mother otter pushed the little female into the woods. Sleeky started after the man. But he was tired after his fight. He could not move as fast as the man. Before he even got to the man, the man did something very surprising! He opened the trap to let the cub go. Then he picked up his dog and ran a little way away from the cub. Then the man stopped again to see what would happen next.

Sleeky did not even seem to see the man. He was much too busy nosing his cub to see that he was all right. Now that he was with his cub, he did not want to chase the man. He had what he wanted! He picked the cub up in his mouth and carried him to his mate. Then, slowly, the little family headed down the stream.

The man watched until the otters could be seen no longer. He was very happy that he had saved the cub. For this man was John Miller, a game warden. It was his job to watch over the animals of these woods. John was happy to see this otter family. There were not many otters left in these woods. Last winter many animals had been trapped for their fur. The game warden was afraid that too many otters had been caught. It was the warden's job to see that no more otters were trapped. One of his first jobs was to take all the traps away from this pond.

Again the warden rubbed his dog's head and ears. "The next job, old boy, should be to take care of you!" he said. "That father otter knows how to fight all right. You found that out the hard way, old boy!"

The man walked away. His voice carried through the woods. "With that father there to take care of them, the otters in that family are all right." At last the man's voice trailed off into the woods.

John Miller could not know that soon the otter family would face a very great danger. This danger would be so great that even the father otter could not stop it. The game warden, himself, would not be able to help. The danger would travel through the woods to every animal there.

5
FIRE!

THE OTTER FAMILY traveled far from the beaver pond. They had to travel slowly because of the little cub's hurt leg. The cub was quite big now. Even so, Sleeky and his mate took turns carrying him. A soft rain was falling. Before night fell, they found a hollow log to sleep in out of the rain. But Sleeky did not let them sleep long. He woke them while it was still night.

The little family followed the father otter through the dark night. He traveled trails that he seemed to know. They all kept close together. Sleeky would not let the cubs make a sound. They were not as safe as when they were near water. He knew that there might be enemy animals in the woods.

That morning they found the place the father was looking for. The rain had stopped. The sun shone warm and bright on a large stream. The stream splashed and bubbled over rocks and around rocks. It made little pools of white bubbles in some places.

Far down the stream, the water ran over some high rocks. It made a roaring sound as it fell into a big pool. Here the cubs could learn to swim through bubbling, roaring waters. This would help them grow stronger. They could play in the pool. There were big trees and rocks all about. There were many fish and frogs to catch and many good places to sleep near the pool.

The otter family stayed in this place until the end of summer. It had been a very hot summer, with little rain. The woods needed rain. They were much too dry. Where the stream had splashed over rocks, it now ran slowly and quietly. The big otters made many trips to other streams looking for one that was not getting dry. They found that all the streams were drying. In some there was very little water.

More dry, hot days passed. Still there was no sign of rain. The burning sun had dried the grass. Many trees had turned brown. Now there was no water at all in the smaller streams. There was hardly any water in the ponds and larger streams.

One day, the hot sun shone on a piece of glass in the woods. A broken glass had been left on the ground. The sun shone through the broken glass. The dry grass under it grew hotter and hotter. Soon a little smoke came from the grass. Then there was a bright flame! The flame caught the dry grass around it. The grass burned quickly. It carried the fire to a pile of leaves. Then the fire jumped to a small tree. Soon the fire was burning from tree to tree. It traveled fast through the woods.

At this time the otter family was on one of its trips. They were away from water. The mother was the first to smell the smoke. When she smelled the air, her fur stood straight up. She coughed a warning. Then the other otters smelled the smoke, too. They all began to run back to the pool.

The nearer they got to the pool, the more smoke there was. The fire was between them and the water!

They turned around and headed back through the woods. Other animals were running, too! There were squirrels, bears and bobcats. Some ran in front of them. Some ran by their side. A bobcat passed close by them. But the bobcat did not even seem to see them.

The sun was covered by dark smoke. The otters did not follow any trails they knew. They ran as fast as they could through the woods. Their one thought was to get away from the smoke and flames.

The warning hiss of burning trees and grass was getting closer and closer. The cries of birds and of running animals sounded in the woods. All the animals were running from the roaring flames. As the trees burned, flaming sticks fell to the ground and started new fires. When the otters ran around these fires, they could not find each other.

Sleeky ran on alone. Once one of his legs caught in a pile of sticks. He fell to the ground. The strong smoke made Sleeky's eyes water. He could hardly see. Smoke was so strong he could hardly breathe. He coughed and coughed. He wanted to stay there and close his eyes for a moment. But the fire was getting closer all the time. The air around him grew very warm. Sleeky pulled himself up and again ran on. He saw other animals bounding through the woods. Bears and bear cubs and even squirrels ran right behind. Small animals ran next to big animals. Each living thing seemed to think only of himself in the hunt for a safe place. The greatest of enemies ran side by side. Each animal hardly knew that the others were there.

At last Sleeky found water. He jumped into a big stream. Many other animals were already there. Even squirrels and other animals that did not like water had jumped into the stream.

The fire passed over the stream. Through the night it burned in the woods close by. At last it burned out in some places. Fire fighters were able to put it out in others. But by the time it was safe to go back to the woods, there were no woods left. By morning only smoke could be seen. Only burned sticks of trees were left to show that here there was once a woods. Many animals had been saved by the stream. Even though they had been saved, their lives were not going to be the same as before. It would be many, many months before animals could live and find food in these woods.

Sleeky, though, could always find enough to eat. He could follow what was left of the streams. There he could find water insects, frogs, or fish. But even though he had enough food to live on, Sleeky was not happy. He could not find his family. He felt very much alone.

Always, Sleeky looked and looked for his mate and cubs. When he was on land he had to be very careful. There were no longer many safe, covered places in the woods. And there were many hungry animals that would be quick to catch an otter. Had his family been burned by the fire? Had they been caught by hungry animals? Sleeky kept on looking for them.

Then one day he came back to the empty beaver pond. It had been burned on one side only. There, in the pond, he found his mate and the young female. They rubbed noses and chattered and rolled in the water. They were very, very happy to be together.

Summer turned to fall. And soon there were signs of winter in the air. The otters played and fished and wandered as always. Sleeky seemed very happy. But his mate still looked for the male cub.

They did find other otters, but not the young male. Then one day, just before winter, the young female went off alone. She did not come back. She was now big enough to start life alone.

At last the mother otter knew that her other cub would not come back. He, too, was big enough to face life alone. He did not need his mother and father to take care of him any longer.

Once again Sleeky and his mate were alone. As they traveled up and down streams, the mother no longer looked for her cubs. She would soon start to look for another nest. Just as the woods would start to grow again next spring, so she would have a new family. She would have new cubs to feed and care for.

As Sleeky and his mate made their first slide in the winter snow, they were very happy. Life seemed good to them. An otter's life was a happy life after all.

EXERCISES

Chapter One

THE CUBS

Choose the right ending for each of these sentences.

1. When they saw Miller's Pond, the otters
   a) swam under the water.
   b) started to play games in the water.
   c) swam to the pond as fast as they could.
2. At the mud bank Sleeky started to
   a) make a nest.
   b) hunt for food.
   c) make a trail that went down to the water.
3. The otters were the only animals in the woods that
   a) were not sleeping.
   b) were afraid of winter.
   c) were not busy getting ready for winter.
4. When winter came, Sleeky and his mate
   a) went south where it was warm.
   b) found new games to play in the snow.
   c) went to sleep, safe from the cold and snow.
5. The otters never felt the cold because
   a) they stayed in their nest on the coldest days.
   b) they kept busy all the time.
   c) the fat under their fur helped keep them warm.

6. The female otter made her nest
   a) at the bottom of a pond.
   b) in an old muskrat nest.
   c) in a hollow log.

7. Sleeky could not understand why his mate
   a) liked the empty muskrat nest so much.
   b) wanted to look for a new pond.
   c) was afraid of the snow.

8. Just before Sleeky's mate had her cubs, she
   a) wanted to be with Sleeky all the time.
   b) liked to play more than ever.
   c) wanted to be alone most of the time.

9. Sleeky was not angry with his mate any more because
   a) he knew she was now a mother.
   b) he had found another otter to play with.
   c) she soon let him stay in the nest with her.

10. When Sleeky first saw the bobcat on the bank, he
   a) was frightened and swam away.
   b) watched to see what the bobcat would do.
   c) brought him a big, fat fish.

Chapter Two

MANY CLOSE CALLS

Choose the right ending for each of these sentences.

1. When Sleeky headed straight for the bobcat
   a) the bobcat was surprised.
   b) the bobcat ran away.
   c) the bobcat jumped into the water.
2. Sleeky wanted the bobcat to
   a) play on the snow slide with him.
   b) chase him.
   c) help him catch fish.
3. Sleeky led the bobcat
   a) far away from his mate and her nest.
   b) right into a waiting trap.
   c) to some muskrats in the woods.
4. Sleeky knew that he had found a beaver pond
   a) because many beaver families were in it.
   b) because he saw huts of sticks and mud.
   c) because a sign on the bank told him so.
5. As Sleeky swam closer to the muskrat, he saw that
   a) the muskrat was eating a fish.
   b) the muskrat was swimming into a beaver hut.
   c) the muskrat was caught in a trap.

6. Sleeky began to swim out of the pond the way he had come into it because
   a) he wanted to catch a big fish he had seen.
   b) he had seen no traps there.
   c) he wanted to go back to his mate and her nest.

7. When Sleeky saw the man, he
   a) swam into a beaver hut to hide.
   b) stayed as still as he could.
   c) was so happy that he rolled and turned in the water.

8. The man Sleeky saw was
   a) hunting for bobcats.
   b) looking at his traps.
   c) making a fire on the bank.

9. At last Sleeky grew so afraid that he
   a) swam straight at the man and dog.
   b) was no longer careful and tried to run away.
   c) chattered and called for help.

10. Sleeky ran off into the woods while the man was
    a) trying to keep the dog away from the traps.
    b) trying to pull the dog out of the water.
    c) looking for his gun.

Chapter Three

SLEEKY COMES BACK

Choose the right ending for each of these sentences.

1. The cubs needed to be near their mother because
   a) they were afraid of the dark.
   b) she gave them food and kept them warm.
   c) they did not like to be alone.
2. By the time spring came, the little cubs
   a) were too big to stay in the nest all day.
   b) were big enough to start families of their own.
   c) moved from the nest to the hollow log.
3. When they went into the high grass near the nest,
   a) the cubs found a hungry bobcat.
   b) the cubs found a large snake.
   c) the cubs found another otter.
4. As the mother otter circled around him, the snake
   a) grew tired from watching her.
   b) tried to strike her when she moved near.
   c) waited for the right time to get away.
5. As soon as Sleeky saw what was happening, he
   a) turned around and hurried away.
   b) ran for his cubs and pushed them into the pond.
   c) began to help his mate circle the snake.

6. When Sleeky took his family on a long trip, his mate
   a) was afraid a cub might wander away.
   b) kept running in front of them.
   c) was happy that the cubs would be seeing new places.

7. The first lesson that the mother otter gave her cubs was
   a) how to catch birds.
   b) to eat fish.
   c) to climb trees.

8. The first time the big otters called the cubs to follow them into the water, the cubs
   a) jumped right into the pond.
   b) stayed well away from the water on the bank.
   c) swam as deep as they could.

9. When the cubs fell into the water, they
   a) had never been so afraid of anything.
   b) liked the water at once.
   c) swam as deep as they could.

10. After the cubs had splashed around a little, the big otters
    a) pulled them to the bank by their tails.
    b) pushed them under the water again.
    c) let them climb on their backs.

Chapter Four

INTO A WIDER WORLD

Choose the right ending for each of these sentences.

1. When the cubs had learned to swim, their mother
   a) made them use the tunnel to the pond.
   b) made them use the land tunnel.
   c) made them stay away from the nest.
2. After the cubs climbed on the big otters' backs,
   a) the big otters swam around the pond.
   b) the big otters pushed the cubs off.
   c) the big otters swam under water.
3. When summer came, Sleeky and his mate
   a) began to fight with their cubs.
   b) stayed in the nest where it was not so hot.
   c) felt like wandering once again.
4. When the otter family left the pond, they
   a) went off into the woods.
   b) made a nest under some rocks down the stream.
   c) followed the stream that ran out of the pond.
5. The otter family traveled slowly because
   a) they were very tired.
   b) they stopped often to eat or play.
   c) they were very hungry.

6. Sleeky warned his family not to go into the beaver pond because
   a) another otter family was there.
   b) a man was fishing there.
   c) he was afraid of the traps he had seen there before.

7. When the little male was caught in the trap, Sleeky
   a) wanted him to learn a lesson and left him alone.
   b) picked the cub up and tried to carry him.
   c) ran away from the pond so he would not be caught.

8. The dog came to the pond because
   a) he wanted to know what all the strange sounds were about.
   b) he wanted to fight with the otters.
   c) it was his job to catch small animals.

9. When the man found the trapped cub, he
   a) fired his gun at it.
   b) picked it up and carried it off into the woods.
   c) opened the trap to let the cub go.

10. As a game warden, it was John Miller's job to
    a) watch over the animals of the woods.
    b) see that otters played no games in the woods.
    c) trap as many animals as he could.

Chapter Five

FIRE!

Choose the right ending for each of these sentences.

1. The place that the father otter was looking for was
   a) a good place to hide for a day.
   b) a large stream.
   c) an empty muskrat nest.

2. By swimming through bubbling, roaring waters, the cubs
   a) would grow stronger.
   b) would learn to be afraid of the water.
   c) would be able to run away from the big otters.

3. Because the summer had been so hot and dry,
   a) the otters had many fights.
   b) the otters took off their coats of fur.
   c) the grass was dry and the streams were drying.

4. As the sun shone on a piece of glass in the woods,
   a) the dry grass under it grew hotter and hotter.
   b) the glass looked silver.
   c) Sleeky began to play with it.

5. The mother otter was the first to
   a) see the broken glass.
   b) run back to the pool.
   c) smell the smoke.

6. All the animals in the woods were
   a) running from the roaring flames.
   b) looking up at the sun.
   c) tired because it was so warm.

7. By the time it was safe to go back to the woods,
   a) not many animals wanted to go back.
   b) the woods were just the same as before the fire.
   c) only burned sticks of trees were left.

8. Sleeky had enough food to live on because
   a) he liked to eat burned sticks.
   b) the game warden gave him food.
   c) he could always find water insects, frogs, or fish.

9. When he was on land, Sleeky had to be very careful because
   a) there were no longer many safe, covered places in the woods.
   b) the smoking grass made his eyes water.
   c) the ground was very hot and he could burn his feet.

10. When Sleeky and his mate were once again alone,
    they knew that
    a) the summer was over.
    b) their cubs would not come back.
    c) their cubs would be waiting at the beaver pond.

THE OTTER FAMILY

THE OTTER FAMILY has two main branches. The members of one branch are called sea otters. They live only along the northern part of the Pacific coastline.

In the old days there were thousands, perhaps millions, of sea otters in North America. Trappers came from as far away as Russia, seeking the thick, velvety, dark brown otter hides. So many sea otters were trapped that their branch of the otter family almost disappeared. For the past half century, though, there have been international regulations protecting these animals. These regulations have had good results. For the sea otter herds are building up again.

The other branch of the family, the river otters, make their homes almost everywhere in North America where there are streams or rivers. It is small wonder that the river otter likes to be near water. He is the best fisherman in the animal world!

SEA OTTER

Some people who like to fish think the otter is too skilled at fishing. They think that otters catch too many trout and other kinds of game fish. On the other hand, the otters also kill the enemies of game fish. Crayfish, bullheads, frogs, and watersnakes all have a habit of eating the eggs of game fish. By killing great numbers of those water creatures, the otters save millions of game-fish eggs each year.

The full-grown river otter is about four feet long. He has a small head, short legs, and big webbed feet with five claws on each foot. His tail is long, about one third of his total length, and tapers from body width to a mere point. This makes him look very streamlined. The strong tail, covered with sleek, dark fur, is extremely useful. When the otter swims, the tail is his rudder. On land, the otter's tail and hind legs can be used as a sort of built-in chair from which he can stretch up and look around.

RIVER OTTER

When a river otter swims near the surface of the water, he uses all four of his short legs. When he dives deep, however, he holds his hind legs back, as a seal does. He uses only his front legs and his tail for deep-water swimming.

On land, a river otter moves with a kind of jumping run. In spite of the shortness of his legs, he can run fast. He may cover as much as twenty-five miles in a week! His long tail drags behind him, leaving marks on the ground or the snow.

Otters have two growths, or layers, of fur. When an otter first comes out of the water, the wet outer fur holds down the dry under fur. Then the little animal looks smooth and sleek and shiny. After he has been out of the water for a while, his fur dries and looks thick and bushy. The fur on his back and tail is thick and dark brown. The fur on his underside is lighter in color. Around his mouth and throat, the fur looks almost white.

ON LAND, OTTERS USE THEIR TAILS
AND HIND LEGS AS BUILT-IN CHAIRS.

IN THE WATER, A RIVER OTTER'S TAIL
SERVES HIM AS A RUDDER WHEN HE SWIMS.

Sometimes called "the clowns of the wild," river
otters seem to enjoy life. Intelligent, playful, and
friendly, they like nothing better than to go sliding on
a muddy or icy hillside. Parents and cubs alike have a
wonderful time at this game. They play it together for
hours at a time.

Otters like to play at fighting, too, but they never
bite or hurt one another. In fact, otter mothers and
fathers and brothers and sisters all seem to get along
well together. They seem to like to be together, even
when it is not necessary for their protection. The only
time the family is separated is when the cubs are born,
in early spring. For three months the mother guards
the cubs so closely that even their father cannot get
near them. When it is time for the young ones to learn
to swim and hunt, however, the father takes a hand.
After that the whole family plays together, hunts together, fishes together, and travels together.

So far as is known, no sea otter has ever been tamed. The friendly river otters, however, make wonderful pets, especially if they are caught and trained when they are very young. Pet otters get along well, not only with their masters but with other household pets as well. Pet dogs and pet otters may take a little while to get acquainted, but after that they play happily together.

Because they are intelligent animals, river otters respond well to training. Some are trained for hunting, just as dogs are trained. Others are trained to catch fish for their masters. A Swedish cook who lived long ago had a famous pet otter. The cook would signal the otter. The otter would run to a nearby fish pond. In a matter of minutes, back would come the otter, carrying a fish for the cook to prepare!

BADGER

MINK

King James the First of England had a whole group of trained otters. He even had a special court official to take care of them. The official's title was "Keeper of the King's Otters."

River otters and sea otters have many other relatives. Among them are the mink, the badger, the wolverine, and the skunk. All these animals belong to one general

SKUNK

WOLVERINE

OTTERS ARE SOMETIMES CALLED THE CLOWNS OF THE WILDS.

group called weasels. All of them are fur-bearing, and all of them eat both meat and fish. Of all these many cousins, however, by far the nicest to know are the sleeky, agreeable clowns called river otters.

VOCABULARY

Sleeky the Otter, the second book in the *Wildlife Adventure Series*, uses a vocabulary of 397 different words for a total of 9,149 running words. All but 12 words, which are italicized in the list below, may be considered basic vocabulary words.

a	be	care	dog
able	bear	careful	down
about	*beaver*	carry	dry
afraid	because	catch	
after	been	caught	each
again	before	chain	ears
air	began	chase	eat
all	behind	chatter	empty
almost	between	circle	end
alone	big	clear	enemy
already	bird	climb	enough
always	bit	close	even
an	*bobcat*	coat	ever
and	body	cold	every
angry	both	come	eyes
animal	*bound*	cough	
another	boy	could	face
any	breathe	cover	fall
anything	bright	cry	family
are	broke	cub	far
around	brown		fast
as	bubble	dam	fat
at	burn	danger	father
ate	busy	dark	feed
away	but	day	feet
	by	deep	fell
back		did	felt
bank	call	dig	*female*
bark	came	do	fight

find	head	land	mouth
fire	hear	large	move
first	heard	last	much
fish	held	lay	mud
flame	help	learn	*muskrat*
follow	her	leave	must
food	here	left	
for	high	leg	
found	him	lesson	near
frogs	himself	let	need
from	his	life	nest
front	hollow	lift	never
fun	hot	like	new
fur	how	little	next
	hungry	live	night
game	hunt	log	no
get	hurt	long	nose
glass	hut	look	not
go		loud	now
good	ice		
got	in	made	of
grass	insects	make	off
great	into	male	often
grew	it	man	old
ground		many	on
grow	job	*mate*	once
gun	John	middle	one
	jump	might	only
had	just	milk	open
happen		Miller	or
happy	keep	moment	other
hard	kept	month	*otter*
hardly	kind	more	out
have	knew	morning	outside
he	know	mother	over

pass	seen	stick	to
paw	shadow	still	together
picked	sharp	stood	too
piece	she	stop	took
pile	shone	straight	top
place	show	strange	*trail*
play	side	stream	trap
pond	sign	*strike*	*travel*
pool	silver	strong	tree
pull	Sleeky	summer	trip
push	sleep	sun	try
put	slid	surprise	tunnel
	slide	swallow	turn
quick	slip	swam	two
quiet	slow	swim	
quite	small		under
	smell	take	understand
rain	smoke	teeth	until
ran	smooth	than	up
ready	snake	that	
right	snow	the	very
roar	so	their	voice
rock	soft	them	
roll	some	then	wait
room	something	there	walk
rub	sometimes	these	*wander*
run	soon	they	want
	sound	thing	*warden*
safe	spike	think	warm
said	splash	this	warn
same	spring	though	was
save	squeak	thought	watch
saw	squirrels	through	water
see	start	time	way
seem	stay	tire	

well	where	winter	world
went	while	with	would
were	whistle	without	
wet	white	woke	yet
what	why	woods	you
when	wide	work	young